MW00653595

This book belongs to:

Printed in Shenzhen, China
July 2024
Print Run: PUR404361

My Favorite Bible Verses Coloring for Girls

Copyright © 2024 by Christian Art Kids, an imprint of Christian Art Publishers,
PO Box 1599, Vereeniging, 1930, RSA

First edition 2024

Cover designed by Christian Art Kids
Designed by Christian Art Kids

Images used under license from Shutterstock.com

Scripture quotations marked NIV are taken from the Holy Bible, New International Version®, NIV® Copyright © 1973, 1978, 1984, 2011 by Biblica, Inc.® Used by permission of Zondervan. All rights reserved worldwide. www.zondervan.com

Scripture quotations marked NLT are taken from the Holy Bible, New Living Translation, copyright © 1996, 2004, 2015 by Tyndale House Foundation. Used by permission of Tyndale House Publishers, Carol Stream, Illinois 60188. All rights reserved.

Scripture quotations marked ESV are taken from the Holy Bible, English Standard Version®. ESV® Text Edition: 2016. Copyright © 2001 by Crossway, a publishing ministry of Good News Publishers. Used by permission. All rights reserved.

Scriptures quotations marked ICB are quoted from the International Children's Bible®, copyright ©1986 1988, 1999, 2015 by Tommy Nelson. Used by permission.

Printed in China

ISBN 978-0-638-00228-7 (Wirebound)
ISBN 978-0-638-00241-6 (Paperback)

© All rights reserved. No part of this book may be reproduced in any form without permission in writi from the publisher, except in the case of brief quotations in critical articles or reviews.

24 25 26 27 28 29 30 31 32 33 – 10 9 8 7 6 5 4 3 2 1

My Favorite Bible Verses

COLORING

FOR GIRLS

The LORD delights
in those who fear Him,
who put their hope in
His unfailing love.
Psalm 147:11 NIV

I will PRAISE You, Lord,
WITH ALL MY HEART.
Psalm 9:1 NLT

"Blessed
are those who
hear the
word of God
and keep it!"
Luke 11:28 ESV

BE JOYFUL.
Encourage each other.
Live in HARMONY
and PEACE.
Then the God of
LOVE AND PEACE
WILL BE
WITH YOU.
2 Corinthians 13:11 NLT

"Peace
I leave with you;
my peace
I give you.
Do not let your hearts
be troubled
and do not
be afraid."
John 14:27 NIV

"Everyone
who calls on
the name of the Lord
will be
saved."
Romans 10:13 NIV

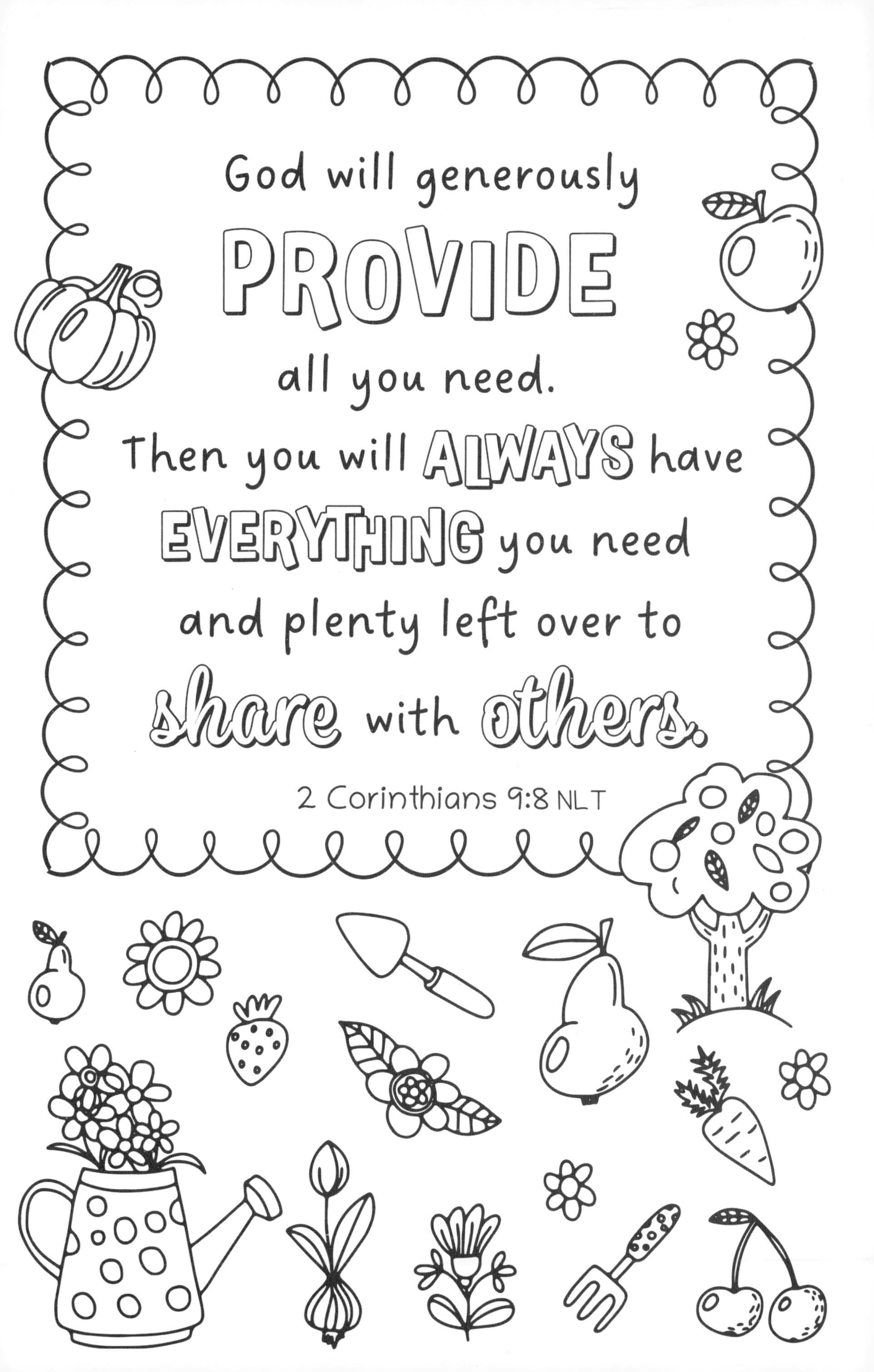
God will generously
PROVIDE
all you need.
Then you will ALWAYS have
EVERYTHING you need
and plenty left over to
share with others.
2 Corinthians 9:8 NLT

"What is
impossible
FOR PEOPLE IS
POSSIBLE
with God."
LUKE 18:27 NLT

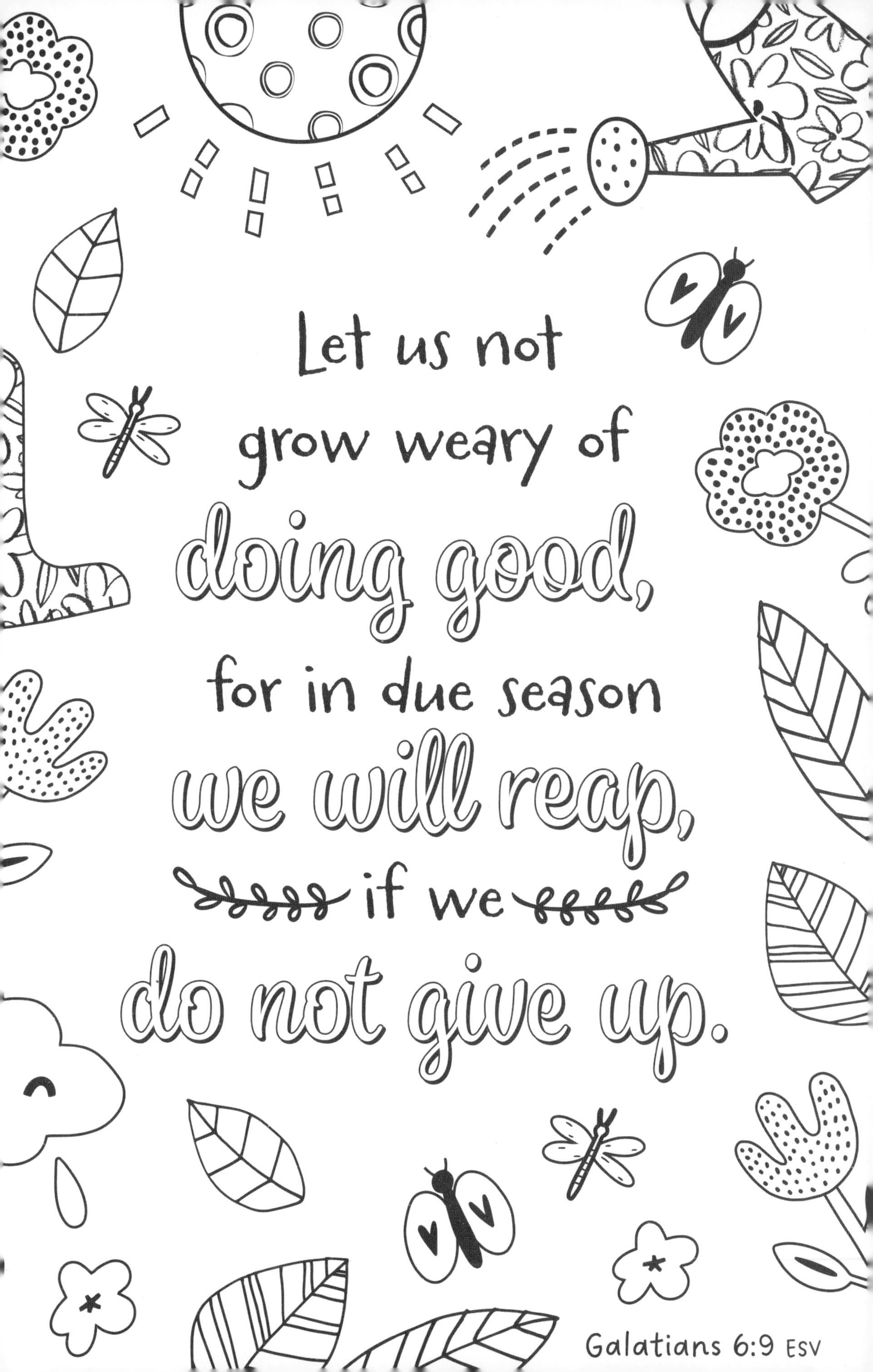
Let us not
grow weary of
doing good,
for in due season
we will reap,
if we
do not give up.
Galatians 6:9 ESV

WALK
in
LOVE
Ephesians 5:2 ESV

My God will **meet** all your **needs**

according to the

riches of His **glory**

in Christ Jesus.

In all the WORK you are doing,
work the BEST you can.

Colossians 3:23 ICB

Draw near to God,
and He will draw near to you.
James 4:8 ESV

The LORD is good to everyone.

HE SHOWERS

COMPASSION

on all His creation.

Psalm 145:9 NLT

Make a joyful
noise to the Lord,
all the earth!
Psalm 100:1 ESV

The LORD is
compassionate
and gracious,
slow to anger,
abounding
in love.
Psalm 103:8 NIV

I can do ALL THINGS THROUGH CHRIST because He gives me STRENGTH.

Philippians 4:13 ICB

The Lord will

guide you continually.

You will be like a

WELL-WATERED GARDEN,

like an

EVER-FLOWING SPRING.

Isaiah 58:11 NLT

The Lord God is like our
SUN AND SHIELD.
The Lord give us
KINDNESS
and glory.
Psalm 84:11 ICB

Great is His love toward us,
and the faithfulness
of the LORD endures forever.

Praise the Lord.

Psalm 117:2 NIV

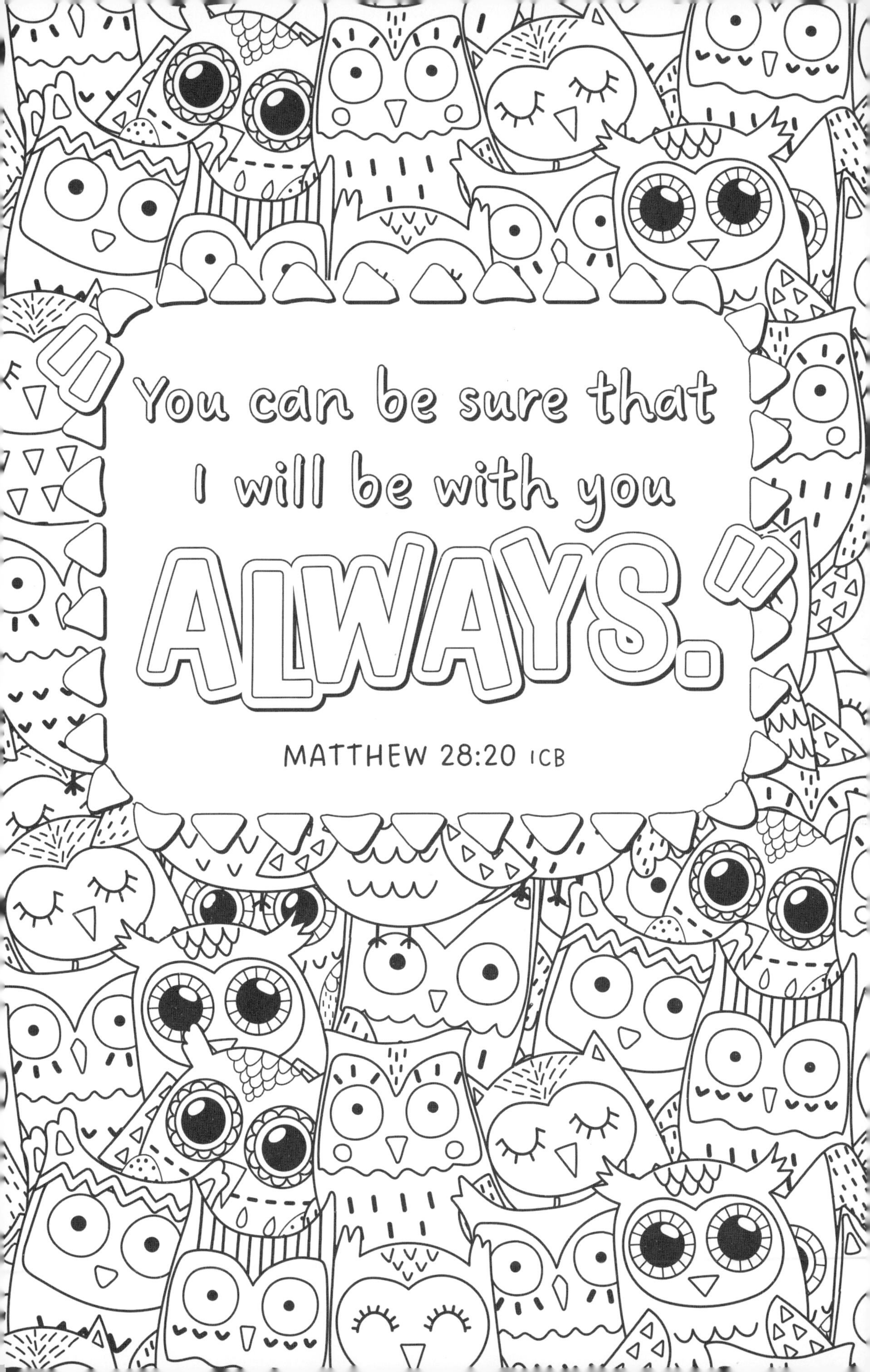
"You can be sure that
I will be with you
ALWAYS."
MATTHEW 28:20 ICB

Jeremiah 31:3 NIV

SEE HOW VERY MUCH OUR FATHER

LOVES US, FOR HE CALLS US

HIS CHILDREN,

AND THAT IS WHAT WE ARE!

1 JOHN 3:1 NLT

"CALL
TO ME
and I will
ANSWER
YOU."
Jeremiah 33:3 ESV

Let
kindness
AND
truth
show
IN ALL YOU DO.
PROVERBS 3:3 ICB

"Your Father KNOWS WHAT YOU NEED before you ask Him."

Matthew 6:8 ESV

He will **COVER** you with His **FEATHERS.**

He will **SHELTER** you with His **WINGS.**

His **FAITHFUL PROMISES** are your **ARMOR** and **PROTECTION.** Psalm 91:4 NLT

We know that in
everything
God works for the
good of those who
love Him.
Romans 8:28 ICB

REJOICE ALWAYS,

PRAY CONTINUALLY,

give thanks

IN ALL CIRCUMSTANCES.

1 Thessalonians 5:16-18 NIV

"IN EVERYTHING,
do to OTHERS
what you would have
THEM do to
YOU."
Matthew 7:12 NIV

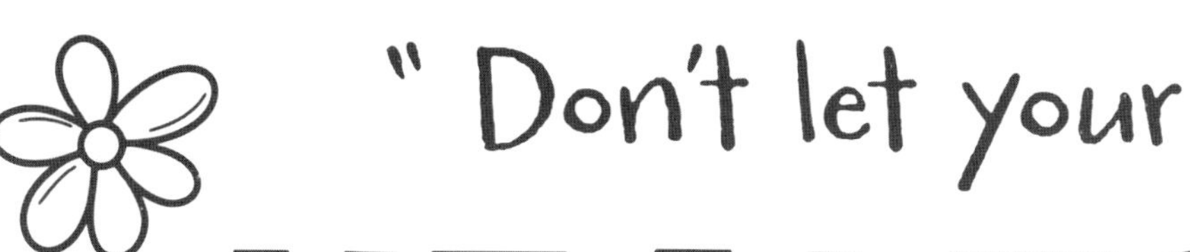

be troubled.
Trust in God,
and trust also in Me."

John 14:1 NLT

LET YOUR
LIGHT
shine!
Matthew 5:16 NIV

Psalm 55:22 NIV
Cast your cares
on the LORD
and He will
sustain you.

The Lord
listens
when I
pray
to Him.
Psalm 4:3 ICB

For the word of the LORD HOLDS TRUE, and we can TRUST everything He does.

Psalm 33:4 NLT

The earth is the LORD's and EVERYTHING in it.

The FRUIT of the SPIRIT is
LOVE, joy, PEACE,
forbearance,
KINDNESS,
GOODNESS,
faithfulness,
GENTLENESS
and SELF-CONTROL.
Galatians 5:22-23 NIV

He tends
His flock like a
SHEPHERD:
He gathers the lambs
in His arms and

carries them
CLOSE
TO HIS HEART.

Isaiah 40:11 NIV

"So do not fear,
for I am WITH YOU.
I will STRENGTHEN
you and HELP you."

COMMIT everything you do to the LORD. Trust Him, and He will help you.

Walk in love.

Ephesians 5:2 ESV

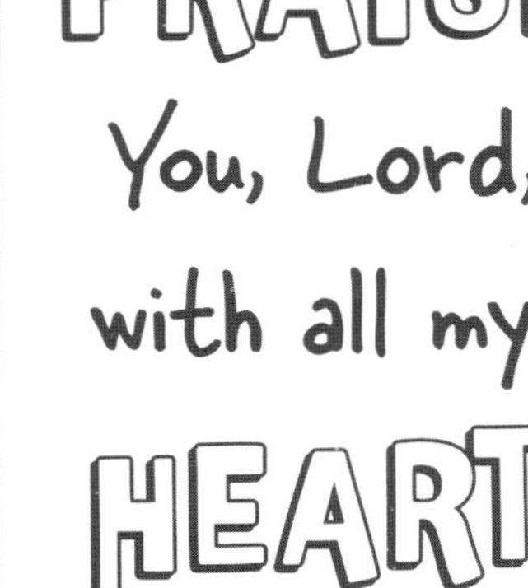

"So do not fear, for I am with you. I will strengthen you and help you."

Isaiah 41:10 NIV

I will **PRAISE** You, Lord, with all my **HEART.**

Psalm 9:1 NLT

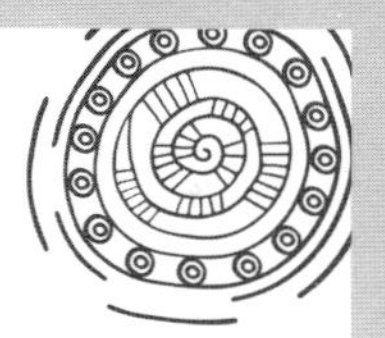

I can do **ALL THINGS** through Christ because **HE GIVES ME STRENGTH.**

Philippians 4:13 ICB

COLOR,
CUT AND SHARE

COLOR,
CUT AND SHARE

In all the
WORK
you are
DOING,
WORK the
BEST
you can.

Colossians 3:23 ICB

The Lord
will keep His
promises.
With love
He takes care
of all He
has made.

Psalm 145:13 ICB

Let
kindness
and
truth
show in all
you do.

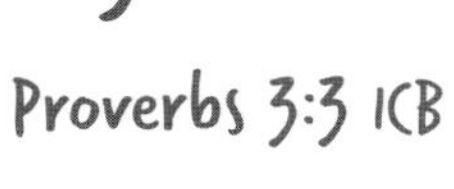

Proverbs 3:3 ICB

Commit
everything
you do
to the Lord.
Trust Him,
and He will
help you.

Psalm 37:5 NLT

COLOR,
CUT AND SHARE

The earth
is the LORD's,
and
everything
in it.
Psalm 24:1 NIV

Give all your
worries
and cares
to God,
for He cares
about you.
1 Peter 5:7 NLT

God,
Your
love
is so
precious!
Psalm 136:7 ICB

Surely Your
goodness
and love
will
follow me
all the days
of my life.
Psalm 23:6 NIV

Let your light shine!

Matthew 5:16 NIV

The Lord LISTENS when I PRAY to Him.

Psalm 4:3 ICB

Nothing in all CREATION will ever be able to separate us from the LOVE of God.

Romans 8:39 NLT

Make a joyful noise to the Lord, all the earth!

Psalm 100:1 ESV

COLOR,
CUT AND SHARE

COLOR, CUT AND SHARE

FOLD

FOLD

FOLD

FOLD

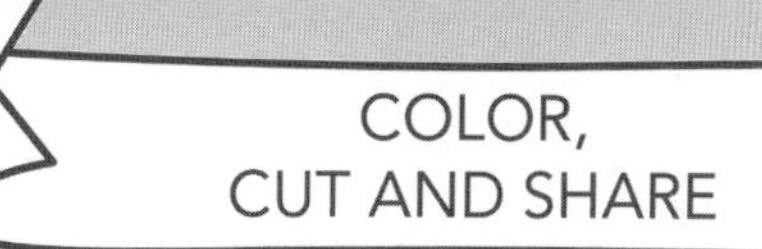
COLOR,
CUT AND SHARE

FOLD

I love you!

Best Friends
Forever

You are precious & loved

FOLD

COLOR,
CUT AND SHARE

FOLD

You Are
Wonderful

Thinking
of you

Especially
for you

FOLD

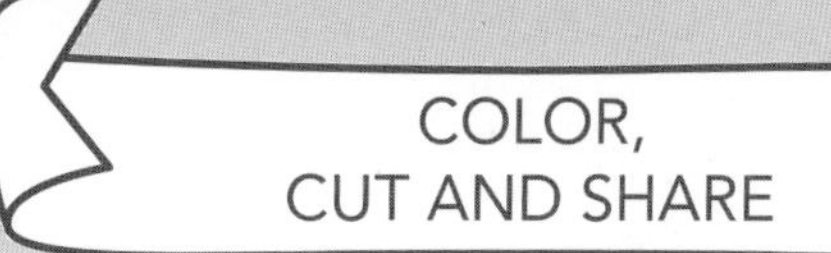

FOLD

Make
TODAY
count!

FOLD

COLOR,
CUT AND SHARE